Wh
Little Mouse
Got
Stuck!

By Ruth Owen

Illustrated by
Emma Bowring

Designed by
Emma Randall

RubY TuesdaY BOOKS

Every day, Little Mouse
was very, VERY busy.

She had repairs to make
to her little nest.

A harvest mouse tears grass into thin strips with her teeth.

She weaves the grass into a nest that's the size of a tennis ball.

She had four **tiny babies** to
lick clean and feed with milk.

Mother harvest mouse

A mother mouse eats her
babies' poo to keep the
family's nest clean.

An eight-day-old
harvest mouse

In real life, a baby harvest
mouse is the size of a
child's thumbnail.

MUNCH . . .

Dandelion seeds

. . . CRUNCH . . .

Harvest mice eat seeds,
buds, nectar from flowers,
blackberries and insects,
such as grasshoppers.

Blackberries

. . . SLURP.

And every day, Little Mouse had to find food.

Life in the hedgerow was **peaceful** and **good**
for **Little Mouse** and her neighbours.

Male chaffinch

Green shield bug →

Chaffinches are
omnivores that feed
on seeds, insects
and spiders.

Peacock
butterfly

← Female
long-tailed tit

Long-tailed tits
weave their nests
from moss, sheep's wool
and spiderwebs.

Knapweed

Honeysuckle

Male bullfinch

Bullfinches feed on seeds, buds and fruit in woodlands, hedgerows and gardens.

Hawthorn

Harvest mouse

An adult harvest mouse weighs the same as a 20p coin.

Dog rose

Bumblebee

Dandelions produce nectar and pollen that bees, butterflies and other pollinators like to eat.

Stinging nettle

Painted lady

Ladybird

Snail

"Give me all the rubbish."

But one day something
BIG came to the hedgerow.

It was noisy and smelly.

The BIG, noisy, smelly thing left something behind. . . .

Sniff Sniff

Little Mouse
could smell
something **good**.

But suddenly, Little Mouse
was **slipping** . . .

. . . and sliding . . .

. . . and tumbling . . .

. . . and . . .

STUCK!

Little mouse
tried to climb,
but it was too
slippery.

She looked for a
way to escape.

But the only way out was high
above her head.

Huddled in their nest,
Little Mouse's tiny babies waited.

They were starting
to **feel hungry**.
Where was their **mother**?

Other animals came to see what the
BIG, noisy, smelly thing had left
behind in the hedgerow.

But they couldn't help Little Mouse.

In their little nest, the
baby mice grew cold.

Their empty tummies
rumbled with hunger.

Little mouse tried to climb,
again and **again**.

But she was **cold**, too.
And very, **very** tired.

Little Mouse curled up
and closed her eyes.
There was **no escape**.

Then suddenly, Little Mouse was flying.

Up and up . . .

. . . higher . . .

. . . and higher.

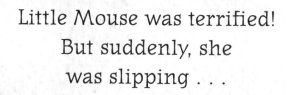

"Gently tip the bottle."

Little Mouse was terrified!
But suddenly, she
was slipping . . .

. . . and sliding . . .

. . . and
tumbling . . .

. . . and FREE!

"Poor little thing.
It must have been terrified."

Little Mouse jumped . . .

. . . and ran . . .

. . . and scurried . . .

. . . as fast as she could.

All the way
home to her nest
and babies.

Little Mouse and her tiny babies
huddled together.

She fed them with milk until their
empty tummies were full.

Inside their nest in
the peaceful hedgerow,
the little mouse family
was warm.

And safe.

Save Our Wildlife!

Every year, thousands of animals are injured or killed by rubbish that's been carelessly thrown away by people.

A blackbird tangled in a face mask

A study discovered that about 8 out of every 100 bottles picked up at the roadside contained the dead body of a trapped mouse, shrew, vole or other small animal.

(Source: Keep Britain Tidy)

The litter that inspired Little Mouse's story!

A trapped hedgehog at a rescue centre

FACT There is NEVER a good reason to throw rubbish from a car.

How Does Litter Harm Animals?

• Small animals, looking for food, can become trapped inside bottles, drinks cans and other containers.

• Drinks cans have sharp edges that may badly cut animals. Broken glass can also cause fatal injuries.

• Animals can be wounded or choked by the plastic rings around cans.

• Animals may suffocate if they try to eat a plastic bag or if they get trapped inside one. Plastic can also get tangled around an animal's body.

Be a Clean-Up Champion!

• Put bottles, cans and other containers into a litter bin or take them home to recycle or throw away safely.

• Cut through all the rings and other sections in plastic can holders. Then recycle the plastic or put it into a bin.

• Whenever possible, replace plastic bags with reusable shopping bags. Fewer plastic bags means fewer dangers to animals.

IF YOU SEE SOME RUBBISH ON THE GROUND:
• Carefully pick it up.
• Recycle or throw it away.
• Sanitise or wash your hands.
• Know you've helped!